FAMILYLIFE® presents

the art of ♥
marriage®

getting to the heart of God's design

FamilyLife Publishing®
Little Rock, Arkansas

The Art of Marriage®
Small-Group Series Workbook
FamilyLife Publishing®
5800 Ranch Drive
Little Rock, Arkansas 72223
1-800-FL-TODAY • FamilyLife.com
FLTI, d/b/a FamilyLife®, is a ministry of Campus Crusade for Christ International®

ISBN: 978-1-60200-512-9

Design: Brand Navigation, LLC
Photography: iStockphoto and BigStock

Printed in the United States of America

First Edition

18 17 16 15 14   2 3 4 5 6

FAMILYLIFE®

contents

the art of ♥ marriage

This small-group series was designed differently from most video marriage curricula, and much effort has been made to pattern this workbook differently as well. What you are holding is not intended simply as a viewer's guide; it's more about giving you a place to process life and capture thoughts while you learn more about marriage.

It is also a place to find more resources for later use. Many people attend a small group, return home, and though they have good intentions of reviewing everything they learned, the book lands on the shelf, never to be opened again. Who hasn't been there? But we hope there is enough in this workbook that you might even want to leave it out on the coffee table and occasionally thumb through it.

Inside, you'll find highlights of key concepts from the video, related articles, group discussion questions, and date-night ideas to build on the big ideas from each session and to help personalize it to *your* marriage.

Marriage is truly an art. Whether you're just about to begin or have been working on your canvas for years, we at FamilyLife believe that with continued effort and God's grace, your relationship can become a masterpiece.

LOVE
Happens

God's Purpose and Plan

the BIG brush strokes

- God designed marriage and has a great plan in mind.

- The primary purpose of marriage is to reflect God's glory.

- It is important to *receive your spouse* as God's perfect gift for you.

3

a kid's perspective[1]

Gwen, age nine: "When I get married I want to marry someone who is tall and handsome and rich and hates spinach as much as me."

Arnold, age six: "I want to get married, but not right away yet because I can't cross the street by myself yet."

Steven, age ten: "I want to marry somebody just like my mother except I hope she don't make me clean up my room."

Bobby, age nine: "First she has to like pizza, then she has to like cheesecake, after that she has to like fudge candy, then I know our marriage will last forever."

top reasons people marry

Love 91%[2]

Companionship 88%

To signify a lifelong commitment 82%

Security for children 79%

To make a public commitment to each other 77%

Legal status or for financial security 66%

Because of religious beliefs 62%

Response to family pressure 50%

Desire for a special occasion 45%

Many people choose marriage for good reasons, yet the divorce rates are still high. Why? Some idealize marriage; others underestimate the amount of effort it really takes to make a relationship work. With so many marriages failing, an increasing number of people are wondering if marriage is even worth the trouble. According to a 2002 survey on marriage and cohabitation,

- Approximately 28 percent of men and women cohabitated before their first marriage.[3]

- Among men and women who considered religion very important, more than 4 in 10 had cohabited at some time in their lives.[4]

"My concept of marriage was totally distorted because of what I knew of the music industry. People get married and divorced all the time. . . . When we got married, we talked about it, and because I had been married once before and divorced, I wasn't sure that I could be the husband I wanted to be. . . . I didn't trust myself. [When] I mentioned that to Julie, I said, 'Well, you know, we'll give it our best, and if it doesn't work, we'll go our separate ways.' And she [said,] 'No! This is it; there is no other one for me. This is the one, and this is the only one.' And I [thought,] 'Wow, what a concept.' It was completely new to me that there wasn't any way out."

—Paul Overstreet, songwriter and musician

If marriage so often ends in disillusionment and failure, why do people get married to begin with?

"[Because] we need a witness to our lives. There's a billion people on the planet. . . . What does any one life really mean? But in a marriage, you're promising to care about everything. The good things, the bad things, the terrible things, the mundane things . . . all of it, all the time, every day. You're saying 'Your life will not go unnoticed because I will notice it. Your life will not go unwitnessed because I will be your witness.'"

—Beverly Clark, from the movie
        Shall We Dance?

"She's got gaps, I got gaps, together we fill gaps."

—Rocky Balboa, from the movie *Rocky*

> "Marriage is embedded in the culture as a gospel testimony that is always making statements. The only question is whether it's a good statement or a bad one."
>
> —Dave Harvey

The **purpose** of **marriage**

- Marriage is not primarily about you.

- It is just as important to **BECOME** the right person as it is to **FIND** the right person.

- The myth of "The One" is not biblical. The one you married is the one with whom you are to make a life.

The **ultimate purpose** of **marriage** is to **reflect** God's image.

- Marriage reflects to the world God's promise to be with us and to redeem us.

- Marriage is a covenant—a permanent promise—not a contract.

- Marriage is more than a device to suit our own needs; it exists for a bigger purpose.

"'Therefore a man shall leave his father and mother and hold fast to his wife, and the two shall become one flesh.' This mystery is profound, and I am saying that it refers to Christ and the church."

—Ephesians 5:31–32

God's plan for marriage

¹⁸ Then the LORD God said, "It is not good that the man should be alone; I will make him a helper fit for him." ¹⁹ So out of the ground the LORD God formed every beast of the field and every bird of the heavens and brought them to the man to see what he would call them. And whatever the man called every living creature, that was its name. ²⁰ The man gave names to all livestock and to the birds of the heavens and to every beast of the field. But for Adam there was not found a helper fit for him. ²¹ So the LORD God caused a deep sleep to fall upon the man, and while he slept took one of his ribs and closed up its place with flesh. ²² And the rib that the LORD God had taken from the man he made into a woman and brought her to the man. ²³ Then the man said, "This at last is bone of my bones and flesh of my flesh; she shall be called Woman, because she was taken out of Man." ²⁴ Therefore a man shall leave his father and his mother and hold fast [cleave] to his wife, and they shall become one flesh.

—Genesis 2:18–24

a unique gift

- Eve's creation was different from the animals' creation; clearly, she was special!

- *Ishah* is the Hebrew word for "woman," and *ish* is the Hebrew word for "man." Adam made a distinction in his naming of Eve.

- Just as Eve was a gift to Adam, your spouse is a **gift** from God to you.

What if I was previously married?

The important thing is *not* to be concerned with the state of any previous marriages but rather to focus on the strength of your commitment to the marriage you are in *today*. You cannot change what happened in the past, but you can begin transforming your present marriage into one that honors Christ.

FamilyLife.com/blended

receiving
your spouse

- "Receiving your spouse" means more than "accepting" him or her; it means you embrace the God-given differences He's built into each of you.

- It's remembering every day that moment you joined together at the altar—each a special gift to the other.

- Your spouse is not your enemy.

- Receiving your spouse is a DAILY choice.

schulte's tips on receiving

- Look for the very tip of the ball, which requires **focus** and **concentration**.

- "Look the ball" **all the way** into your hands, until you have it **firmly grasped**.

- Quickly tuck it into the crook of your arm. Keep looking at it until it is **fully tucked**.

- Finally, **look up** and get set to run! (If you're not already smashed into the ground.)

staying connected in the valley

by Pam Mutz

The loss of a child, and other tragedies, can be very difficult to work through with your spouse. However, many couples find that the process of working through a tragedy draws them closer together. The following are a few ways you can stay connected to your spouse in the midst of heartache:

1) Spend time reading the Word of God both individually and as a couple, particularly the Book of Psalms.

2) Pray together. Use scriptures to enrich your prayer time. Husbands, choose to initiate.

3) Journaling is a concrete way to express to God how you feel and helps a spouse understand your struggle.

4) Worship corporately with other believers, even when you don't feel like it.

5) Join a small group so that others can support and encourage you as you walk through this difficult time.

6) Practice a family tradition that commemorates your loved one, such as releasing balloons into the air or writing a love letter to that person.

7) Choose to find joy in other areas of life, and verbalize a thankful heart. Make a written list of the things you're thankful for. True joy in a family is caught, not taught.

8) Go away together as a couple and regroup. Some things can't be sorted out in the midst of children, jobs, and routine. Take a weekend to process, cry, hold each other, communicate, and rest.

9) Embrace the Holy Spirit as your Comforter, and allow Him to work as you rest.

10) Verbalize your choice to make your attitude better, not bitter.

11) Ask for help from trusted friends or a counselor.

THEREFORE **shall a MAN leave** his **father** and his **mother,** and shall **CLEAVE** unto his **WIFE:** and **THEY** shall be **ONE flesh.**

GENESIS 2:24 (KJV)

receiving your spouse

What are the top three difficulties or problems you've experienced since you've been married?

1)

2)

3)

How have these trials affected your ability to continue receiving your spouse? To view him or her as God's special gift to you?

did i choose the right person?

Some couples, after facing greater problems and differences in personalities than they anticipated, begin to wonder, *Did I choose the right person?* They might think, *Things would be easier if I had just married a person who better understands me.*

But the question is not "Did I *marry* the right person?" Rather, one must ask, "Am I *becoming* the right person?"

"I have no way of knowing whether or not [you] married the wrong [person], but I do know that many people have a lot of wrong ideas about marriage and what it takes to make that marriage happy and successful. I'll be the first to admit that it's possible that you did marry the wrong person. However, if you treat the wrong person like the right person, you could well end up having married the right person after all. On the other hand, if you marry the right person, and treat that person wrong, you certainly will have ended up marrying the wrong person. I also know that it is far more important to *be* the right *kind* of person than it is to marry the right person. In short, whether you married the right or wrong person is primarily up to *you*."

—Zig Ziglar, *Courtship After Marriage*

COMPLETING the Picture

- 🌸 I must receive my spouse as God's perfect gift for me.

- 🌸 I must choose to believe that my spouse is not my enemy.

- 🌸 I must renew my commitment to the permanency of marriage.

- 🌸 I affirm that the primary purpose of my marriage is to reflect the glory of God.

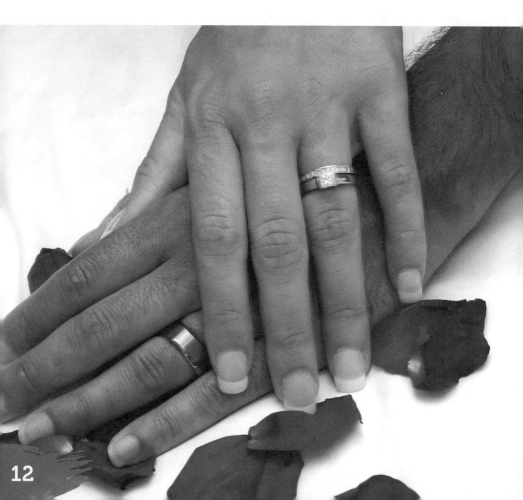

group discussion questions

1) What was the most thought-provoking concept you heard in this session?

2) Name several "good" reasons for getting married. Name several "bad" reasons.

3) On the video, after mentioning some of the reasons that people marry, the point was made that ultimately marriage should "tell the truth about God." Why is this important?

4) Read Ephesians 5:31–33. In what ways should a Christian marriage tell the truth about God (that is, reflect His image and love)?

5) On the video a distinction is made between "accepting" your spouse and "receiving" your spouse. Describe the difference and explain why this is important in your relationship as husband and wife.

6) Share with the group some of the ways that God is using the differences between you and your spouse:

- to shape you as a person
- to make your marriage stronger

Prepare for your next group meeting by looking over pages 16–26 in your workbook..

Date-Night Ideas

- Look through your wedding pictures. Also reread your wedding invitation and vows and talk about the meaning of the words.

- Eat at the restaurant that was your favorite when you were dating, or one similar to it.

- Re-create the day of your proposal as closely as you can.

- Watch your wedding video.

Date-Night Discussion

Before the date, do the following on your own:

1. Review the list of "top reasons people marry" on page 4. What were some of your reasons for getting married?

2. List a few of the specific things that attracted you to your spouse.

3. Read Genesis 2:24 (page 10). What do you think it means to "leave your father and mother"?

4. Do you feel like you really left your parents—emotionally, physically, and financially—and bonded with your spouse? If not, what steps can you take to do so?

5. What are some ways a couple can "cleave" to each other?

6. Part of cleaving is learning to receive your spouse unconditionally, as God's perfect gift for you. Go to page 11 and complete the exercise Receiving Your Spouse.

7. Go back and read the article on page 9, "Staying Connected in the Valley." What one thing from this list would you like to begin practicing in your marriage?

On the Date:

1. Talk about your wedding day and the honeymoon. What are some of your favorite memories? Any funny moments? Anything you would do differently?

2. Talk about how successfully each of you has "left" your parents. Where do you need to make adjustments to continue "leaving" appropriately, in an honorable way?

3. Discuss your answers to question 7 above about "Staying Connected in the Valley."

4. Take time to share your thoughts from other questions that you answered on your own.

5. End your time together by looking each other in the eye and reading the statements from "Completing the Picture" on page 12; then pray together for the wisdom and courage to fulfill any new commitments you've made.

LOVE
Fades

Overcoming Isolation

"We must never be naïve enough to think of marriage as a safe harbor from the Fall. . . . The deepest struggles of life will occur in the most primary relationship affected by the Fall: marriage."

—Dan Allender and Tremper Longman III, *Intimate Allies*

the BIG brush strokes

- Couples naturally drift toward isolation.
- Our differences and weaknesses can push us apart.
- Sin has affected every marriage.
- The gospel brings healing and reconciliation.
- Couples must learn to walk by the power of the Holy Spirit in marriage.

He Said . . .

"I thought I was doing great as a husband. . . . I would have said to you [that] on a scale of 1 to 10, my marriage is probably a 10. If not a 10, it's a 9.8, and I guarantee you my wife would agree." —Dave Wilson

She Said . . .

"And I would have said, 'We're a 1.0, maybe like a 0.5,' and I think he was totally clueless . . . which made me even more angry, because I'm thinking, *How do you not know how bad we're doing?*" —Ann Wilson

Art and marriage are both studies in contrasts: A good painting might combine the bitter shades of brown with the brightest hues of blue. Art draws together the harsh and the soft and holds both in tension. It recognizes the pain, yet it also celebrates the joys of life. Good art requires patience and skill; it is a beauty to behold, and masterpieces are often the fruit of a lifetime of labor. Most marriages begin with the hope of discovery and the joy of sharing life together, yet not every marriage becomes a masterpiece. What happens? What goes wrong?

the drift toward isolation

- One reason couples drift apart is that they fail to make their marriage the priority it ought to be.

- We are culturally conditioned to believe that our happiness ought to be our number-one priority in life.

- Selfishness is one of the root causes of isolation.

"The devil's strategy for our times is to trivialize human existence and to isolate us from one another while creating the delusion that the reasons are time pressures, work demands, or economic anxieties."

—Dr. Phillip Zombardo, "The Age of Indifference," *Psychology Today*

"The good news is that isolation can be defeated. Its disease can be cured if you are willing to make the right choices and then put the necessary effort into building oneness."

—Dennis and Barbara Rainey, *Staying Close*

"Genesis 3 marks the transition from a sinless state of humanity, in union with God and in fellowship with Him and walking with His blessing and approval and pleasure, to a state where there is sin, and Adam and Eve are alienated from God."

—Wayne Grudem

Researcher John Gottman, after interviewing thousands of couples, said that there are four behaviors he calls "The Four Horsemen of the Apocalypse," whose presence in a marriage indicates a high probability of divorce. These behaviors are "criticism, contempt, defensiveness, and withdrawal." Once these behaviors take over, "unless a couple makes changes, they are likely to find themselves sliding helplessly toward the end of their marriage."[1]

free fall by greg ferguson

the serpent
the snake
was the savviest of all of the creatures
in the Creator's perfect planet
the reptile
surveyed the scene with keen snake eyes
streetwise
armed with an arsenal of plausible lies
he slithered up to Eve the Woman
from her blind side
preserving the element of surprise

and he said
hello, child!
how was your day?
I overheard your conversation
I just have one simple question:
exactly what did the Creator say?

that thing about the tree
the evil and the good:
how do you know that you understood?
did he really say what you think you heard
maybe your mind twisted up the words
did he say hands off all the plants
don't look don't touch don't taste
what a waste that would be

Eve the woman pointed out
the tree with the taboo
the tree of the knowing
of the good and evil too
she told the snake
that God had made it drop dead clear
that everything else was free
every other tree
but if they took one tiny taste
of the fruit
of this particular one—
they would absolutely
positively
crash and burn

Ah
said the snake faking genuine concern
the deity's afraid of what you're
gonna learn
with just one bite you'd be just like him

eyes wide open
knowing the heights of what humans can do
knowing the depths, the despicable too
God would have no tactical advantage over you
you and your man
could have the run of the place
total control over the food you eat
the life you live
the path you choose;
with just one small bite
you could gain the whole green world
and that means that God of yours
would lose

the woman Eve walked closer
and closer to the tree
she sniffed and felt the fruit
against her cheek

"totally wise with open eyes"—she said—
what's wrong with that?
"maybe my man and I
were born for this
born to know
born to control
born to rule"

she swallowed hard
and it was done
she gave some
to her covenant partner Adam
he opened his mouth
and gobbled it down
and the universe

was silent

it was the cool part of the day
and God was walking
walking
through the land he made
his ecosystem
so magnificently put together
about to erode
about to implode
before his sad and timeless eyes—
he took one long last look
and kissed the innocence
goodbye

Adam
where you hiding son
Eve
girl what have you done

look around
it's broken now
under a curse
from bad to worse

now your eyes are wise and clear
now you know shame
now you know fear
now you know you're naked
now you run for cover

here's what gonna happen:

life will be shorter
pain will be greater
work will be harder
grinding it out
by the sweat on your brow
the blood on your hands

Eve and Adam
even the bond you have
will now be strained
slightly off
distorted
reframed

and as for you
reptile
snake
Adam will crush your head
you will strike and bite his heel
you will feel the weight
of the consequences of what
you've done for eons

he looked them in the eye
with a sigh
it's broken now, he said

and the serpent

he just smiled

21

Genesis 3:1–16

(emphasis added)

¹Now the serpent was more crafty than any other beast of the field that the LORD God had made.

He said to the woman, "Did God actually say, 'You shall not eat of any tree in the garden'?" ²And the woman said to the serpent, "We may eat of the fruit of the trees in the garden, ³but God said, 'You shall not eat of the fruit of the tree that is in the midst of the garden, neither shall you touch it, lest you die.'" ⁴But the serpent said to the woman, "You will not surely die. ⁵For God knows that when you eat of it your eyes will be opened, and you will be like God, knowing good and evil." ⁶So when the woman saw that the tree was good for food, and that it was a delight to the eyes, and that the tree was to be desired to make one wise, she took of its fruit and ate, and she also gave some to her husband who was with her, and he ate.

THE RESULTS OF THEIR SIN WERE . . .

Shame

⁷Then the eyes of both were opened, and they knew that they were naked. And they sewed fig leaves together and made themselves loincloths.

Guilt

⁸And they heard the sound of the LORD God walking in the garden in the cool of the day, and the man and his wife hid themselves from the presence of the LORD God among the trees of the garden.

Fear

⁹But the LORD God called to the man and said to him, "Where are you?" ¹⁰And he said, "I heard the sound of you in the garden, and I was afraid, because I was naked, and I hid myself."

Blame Shifting

¹¹He said, "Who told you that you were naked? Have you eaten of the tree of which I commanded you not to eat?" ¹²The man said, "The woman whom you gave to be with me, she gave me fruit of the tree, and I ate." ¹³Then the LORD God said to the woman, "What is this that you have done?" The woman said, "The serpent deceived me, and I ate."

¹⁴The LORD God said to the serpent,

"Because you have done this,
cursed are you above all livestock
and above all beasts of the field;
on your belly you shall go,
and dust you shall eat
all the days of your life."

Battle for Control

¹⁵"I will put enmity between you and the woman,
and between your offspring and her offspring;
he shall bruise your head,
and you shall bruise his heel."
¹⁶To the woman he said,
"I will surely multiply your pain in childbearing;
in pain you shall bring forth children.
Your desire shall be for your husband,
and he shall rule over you."

the **fallout**
from **the fall**

- Pride and disobedience were behind Adam and Eve's rejection of God's plan in the garden (Genesis 3:1-6).

- By rejecting God's plan, Adam and Eve's relationship, intimacy, and unity with God were broken.

- Sin now infects and affects everyone.

- **A result of sin:** blame shifting. Adam blamed Eve for his own sin. Eve blamed the serpent for her sin. Adam also blamed God ("the woman whom *you* gave to me . . ."[3:12]).

- The result of sin was punishment in three parts:

  - Pain in work (3:17–19)
  - Pain in childbirth (3:16)
  - Pain in marriage relationships (3:16)

- Another result of sin was marital conflict.

- Instead of *completing* each other, Adam and Eve began to *compete* with each other.

- There is a spiritual battle occurring within marriage:

"For we do not wrestle against flesh and blood, but against the rulers, against the authorities, against the cosmic powers over this present darkness, against the spiritual forces of evil in the heavenly places." —**Ephesians 6:12**

"Finally, be strong in the Lord and in the strength of his might. **Put on the whole armor of God,** *that you may be able to stand against the schemes of the devil."* —**Ephesians 6:10–11**

there is an enemy, and it is not your mate.

the problem . . . and the solution

If you want to experience life and marriage the way God designed it, then you need a relationship with Him. If you want to live as the person God intended you to be, then you need to know the God who created you.

Our problem is that sin separates us from Him. Though we may try to earn God's approval by working hard to become better people, we must understand that the problem of sin runs much deeper than bad habits and will take more than our best behavior to overcome. God's Word clearly tells us that we cannot close the gap between ourselves and God on our own:

> *"All we like sheep have gone astray; we have turned every one to his own way."*
>
> —Isaiah 53:6

> *"There is a way that seems right to a man, but its end is the way to death."*
>
> —Proverbs 14:12

> *"The wages of sin is death."*
>
> —Romans 6:23

God is holy, and we are sinful. No matter how hard we try, we cannot come up with some plan—such as living a good life or trying to do what the Bible says—and hope we can be "good enough" to earn a relationship with God. We need a Savior.

"To be able to look forward to a lifelong, **thriving marriage, you** must have a clear **understanding of the** gospel. Without it, **you cannot see God,** yourself, or your **marriage for what** they truly are. The **gospel is the fountain** of a thriving marriage."

—Dave Harvey,
When Sinners Say "I Do"

Thankfully, God has provided the way to solve our dilemma. He became a man in the person of Jesus Christ. Jesus lived a holy life in perfect obedience to God and willingly died on a cross to pay the penalty for our sin.

> *"God shows his love for us in that while we were still sinners, Christ died for us."*
>
> —Romans 5:8

> *"The wages of sin is death, but the free gift of God is eternal life in Christ Jesus our Lord."*
>
> —Romans 6:23

The life, death, and resurrection of Jesus has provided the only way to establish a relationship with God. Receiving Christ means that we trust Christ to forgive our sins and make us the kind of people He wants us to be. It's not enough to just intellectually acknowledge that Christ is the Son of God. As an act of the will, we must place our faith and trust in Him and surrender our lives to Him and His plan for us:

> *"For by grace you have been saved through faith. And this is not your own doing; it is the gift of God, not a result of works, so that no one may boast."*
>
> —Ephesians 2:8–9

When we accept the incredible gift God offers us, we become His children:

> *"But to all who did receive him, who believed in his name, he gave the right to become children of God."*
>
> —John 1:12

"**The gospel of Christ crucified for our sins is the foundation of our lives. Marriage exists to display it. And when marriage breaks down, the gospel is there to forgive and heal and sustain until He comes, or until He calls.**"

—John Piper,
This Momentary Marriage

COMPLETING  the *Picture*

🍂 I must learn how to resist the natural drift toward isolation in marriage.

🍂 My individual sin is the issue behind marital conflict. I must learn to take responsibility for my sin and reconcile with God.

🍂 Jesus Christ's sacrifice reconciled me to God and allows me to live in peace with Him and others.

🍂 I must learn to walk each day by the power of the Holy Spirit in order to stay close to my spouse.

group discussion questions

1) What was the most thought-provoking concept you heard in this session?

2) On the video, Dave and Ann Wilson mentioned the significantly different rating they would have each given their marriage–Dave would have rated it at 9.8 and Ann would have rated it at 0.5!

   - Why were their ratings so far apart?

   - Do you think this is typical, that one spouse thinks their marriage is doing much better than the other spouse does?

   - If you believe this is typical, why do you think it is so?

3) The point was made that couples drift apart because they've not made their marriage a priority. Practically speaking, what can a husband do to prioritize his marriage? What can a wife do?

4) Think about some of the couples whose marriages you admire. What do you see them doing to build oneness in their relationship?

5) Read Genesis 2:20–25. This passage describes the great state of marriage as God intended it—filled with gratitude for each other and the recognition that God brought the two of them together. But sin enters the picture in Genesis 3.

   - Describe the effects that sin has on marriage.

   - How should you deal with personal sin in order to guard the oneness of your marriage?

   - What role does God have in your marriage?

6) On the video, the sobering point is made that Satan is actively trying to destroy your marriage, that he—and not your spouse—is your enemy.

   - Identify some of the tactics you see Satan using to attack marriages in our culture.

   - Discuss some of the things you can do to protect your marriage and the marriages of your friends and loved ones.

Prepare for your next group meeting by looking over pages 30–46 in your workbook.

Date-Night Ideas

- As a couple, have a picnic in an isolated place (a field, an empty parking lot, an empty beach).

- Spend two hours on the couch together one evening without TV, cell phones, computers, or the Internet. Spend time together talking, reading to each other, or just sitting quietly together.

Date-Night Discussion

Before the date, do the following on your own:

1. List some of the things that commonly cause couples to drift apart; then identify anything that might be causing you and your spouse to drift apart.

2. Describe the role you believe God has in keeping your marriage together.

3. Read Genesis 3:1–16. List the ways sin affected the relationship between the first husband and wife.

4. Review the results of sin that are described on page 22. Have you noticed any of these tendencies in your life? Would your spouse say that you struggle in any one particular area? Take a moment and repent and ask God to forgive you for giving in to this sin. Pray for the strength to break free from the bondage of sin.

5. Read pages 24–25. Are things right between you and God? Have you received Christ, trusted Him to forgive all your sins and make you a new person? You can talk to Him right now. If talking to God is new to you, here is a suggested prayer to guide you:

> *Lord Jesus, I need You. Thank You for dying on the cross for my sins. I receive You as my Savior and Lord. Thank You for forgiving my sins and giving me eternal life. Make me the kind of person You want me to be. Amen.*

6. How could you and your spouse incorporate God more into your lives and your marriage?

On the Date:

1. Take turns describing one thing your spouse could do this week to help you feel closer to him or her.

2. Explain your response to question 1 that you answered on your own; then discuss some ideas for stopping the drift in your relationship.

3. Share any spiritual commitments you made while working on the first six questions on your own.

4. Pray together that God would give you the wisdom and courage to address any area that has caused you to drift apart.

LOVE
Dances

Fulfilling Our Responsibilities

"Wives, understand and support your husbands in ways that show your support for Christ. . . . Husbands, go all out in your love for your wives, exactly as Christ did for the church. . . . This is a huge mystery, and I don't pretend to understand it all."

—Excerpts from Ephesians 5, *The Message*

the BIG brush strokes

- God designed different responsibilities for men and women in marriage.

- Though their responsibilities are different, men and women are still equal in value.

- God calls men to sacrificially love and lead their wives.

- God calls women to respect and support their husbands.

the dance

Fred Astaire and Ginger Rogers, who made ten films together, are often recognized as the most famous dancing duo in American film history. However, Astaire was initially reluctant to dance with Rogers, preferring to avoid becoming part of a dance team.

According to Astaire, when they were first teamed together, "Ginger had never danced with a partner before. She faked it an awful lot . . . but Ginger had style and talent and improved as she went along. She got so that after a while everyone else who danced with me looked wrong."[1]

Part of what made their performance so attractive was that Ginger Rogers "so convincingly conveyed . . . that [dancing with Fred Astaire was] the most thrilling and satisfying experience imaginable."[2]

Rogers and Astaire were world-class dancers—masters of their art—yet there is much to learn from their craft that applies to marriage. For instance, good dancing requires that each person know his or her role and play it well.

role confusion

- Culture has created a "gender blender" when it comes to roles and responsibilities in a marital relationship.

- Someone has to take the lead in a relationship.

- Many couples begin marriage with a 50/50 approach to the relationship.

> **"A person [who] says** *'I'll meet you halfway'* **is a poor judge of** distance."
>
> **—Michael Easley**

reasons the 50/50 plan is destined to fail[3]

1) **Acceptance is based on performance.** For many people, performance becomes the glue that holds the relationship together, but it isn't really glue at all. It's more like Velcro. It seems to stick, but it comes apart when a little pressure is applied.

2) **Giving affection is based on merit.** With the "meet me halfway" [50/50] approach, a husband would give affection to his wife only when he felt *she had earned it*. She, in turn, would lavish affection and praise only when she felt *he had earned it*.

3) **Motivation for action is based on feeling.** As a newlywed, it's easy to act sacrificially because the pounding heart and romantic feelings fuel the desire to please. But what happens when those feelings diminish? If you don't feel like doing the right thing, perhaps you won't do it at all.

4) **Rejection is based on focusing on weakness.** One spouse often focuses on how the other spouse is not doing his or her "half." Both constantly fall short of halfway because each person defines the midpoint differently. Ask a husband or wife to list his or her spouse's strengths in one column and the weaknesses in another, and the weaknesses will usually outnumber the strengths five to one.

equal value, different roles

There are many areas in life in which we are called upon to play a role that is different from the role others are playing. It's true at work, at school, at church, in sports, and in community organizations. A football team is a classic example: Each player has a different job, and every job is important. If someone misses an assignment, the quarterback can get his head knocked off! And although he is often paid the most, the quarterback is the first to acknowledge that he could not do his job without the offensive linemen.

"When two people are on a horse, one of them has to be in front."

—Dennis Rainey

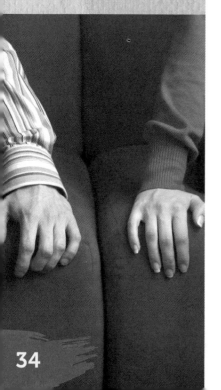

The Family Manifesto: FamilyLife created *The Family Manifesto* to provide families with a Scripture-based blueprint for building godly homes. The document supports the conviction that the family is the backbone of the Christian church and of society as a whole. The manifesto, which can be read in its entirety on the Family-Life website is a declaration of values to help couples uphold, strengthen, and continue to build upon the biblical institutions of marriage and family.

The Family Manifesto on marriage: We believe that God created marriage for the purpose of couples glorifying God as one flesh, parenting godly children, and enjoying sexual pleasure. "As iron sharpens iron" (Proverbs 27:17, NIV), we believe that God uses marriage to sharpen a man and a woman and mold them into the image of Jesus Christ. Just as the Trinity reflects the equal worth of Father, Son, and Spirit, with differing roles, we believe that God created a man and a woman with equal worth but with differing roles and responsibilities in marriage.

defining a husband's role

- A husband's privileged role is to love his wife as Christ loved the church.

    "Husbands, love your wives, as Christ loved the church and gave himself up for her."

    —Ephesians 5:25

- To do this a husband has to know his wife, pay attention to her, nurture her, cherish her.

    "For no one ever hated his own flesh, but nourishes and cherishes it, just as Christ does the church."

    —Ephesians 5:29

- The husband is called to be the head of his wife, just as Christ is head of the church.

    "For the husband is the head of the wife even as Christ is the head of the church."

    —Ephesians 5:23

- "Headship" means that the man sacrifices himself—his needs, desires, dreams—for the sake of his family.

- "Headship" also means that the man has the burden of taking the initiative to move things forward on behalf of his family.

    "My role is to live to make my wife great."

    —Crawford Loritts

According to a Yahoo! HotJobs' survey,[4] some of the qualities for being a good leader (in order of importance) are . . .

1) Communication and listening skills

2) Effective leadership skills

3) Trust in their employees to do their job well

4) Flexibility and understanding

5) Teamwork skills

6) Even temperament

7) Interest in employee development

8) Ability to share credit

how a husband nourishes and cherishes his wife[5]

by Barbara Rainey

- Seek to understand her role and her struggle.

- If she works outside the home, understand her job and the pressures it places on her, especially regarding her role at home.

- Verbalize often, especially during her times of failure and discouragement, your complete acceptance of her. (Be sure that you really *do* accept her.)

- Liberally verbalize belief in her as a person and in her ability and worth.

- Verbalize your need for her, and back it up by sharing with her your fears, failures, needs, dreams, hopes, and discouragements. Do it cautiously if this is new to you.

- Share at times when she can listen attentively and appreciate your transparency. (Don't share something serious when she's preoccupied with the kids or dinner.)

- Notice and praise her for the things she does for you (meals, laundry, etc.).

- Be willing to help her work through difficulties in her life: discipline, problems with the children, relationships with friends and parents, fears, resentment, etc.

- Be patient and realize that nourishing and cherishing is a lifetime process.

the meaning of *kephale* ("head")

Dr. Wayne Grudem, in his effort to defend a biblical view of roles in marriage, sought to inspect every use of the Greek word *kephale*, which is translated "head" in Ephesians 5:23. He found 2,336 occurrences of the word in ancient Greek literature, and in *every* instance, it was used to mean "authority over/ruler." He went on to assert that "no examples have ever been found where person A is called the 'head' of person B and person A is not in a position of authority over person B."[6]

what does it mean for a husband to be the head of his wife?

Many women have a hard time accepting the teaching that the husband is the "head" of the wife because they have witnessed the abuse of this role. Some men, after hearing they are the "head" of their wives, have understood this to mean that a man can order his wife around and treat her like a slave. No man who reads Ephesians 5:23–30 could reasonably come to such a conclusion.

But when a biblical principle is misused, it does not inherently mean that the concept is faulty. The apostle Paul calls a man to lead as Christ leads the church, sacrificially, treating his wife as his own body. He should nourish and cherish her and cleanse her "by the washing of water with the word" (verse 26). The language here is very gentle and caring. No man could truly fulfill his responsibility as the leader of his home without learning to lovingly sacrifice his own life for the sake of his wife.

on your own

What are five ways I could sacrifice more for my wife?

1)

2)

3)

4)

5)

The Family Manifesto for husbands:

We believe God has charged each husband with fulfilling the responsibility of being the "head" (servant leader) of his wife. We believe God created a man incomplete, and as a husband, he needs his wife as his helper. We believe a husband will give account before God for how he has loved, served, and provided for his wife. We reject the notion that a husband is to dominate his wife. Likewise, we reject the notion that a husband is to abdicate his responsibilities to lead his wife. Rather, we believe his responsibility is to love his wife. This love is characterized by taking the initiative to serve her, care for her, and honor her as a gift from God. We believe his responsibility is to protect his wife and help provide for her physical, emotional, and spiritual needs.

We also believe a husband is to seek after and highly regard his wife's opinion and counsel and treat her as the equal partner she is in Christ. Therefore, we are committed to exhort and implore men not to abuse their God-given responsibilities as husbands, but rather to initiate a sacrificial love for their wives in the same way Jesus Christ initiated sacrificial love and demonstrated it fully on the cross (Genesis 2:18–25; Ephesians 5:22–33; Colossians 3:19; 1 Peter 3:7; 1 Timothy 5:8).

wayne and margaret grudem: before phoenix[7]

Wayne Grudem's decision to move to Phoenix, Arizona, for his wife's health was done sacrificially, with deep concern for her needs. Loving her in this way was something he learned [not only] from Scripture but also from a mistake he made early in their marriage.

Wayne's first teaching job was at Bethel College in Minneapolis, Minnesota. After almost four years of teaching, he received a call from Trinity Evangelical Divinity School with a job offer.

Wayne said, "Almost immediately I was very interested, because I wanted to train pastors."

Margaret remembers that they discussed it, but she said, "I could tell that his mind was already made up."

They moved to Illinois soon thereafter, but looking back, Wayne says, "I don't think I was very thoughtful of Margaret. . . . She loved it at Bethel, [but] the decision-making process, looking back, wasn't exactly right. And Margaret was hurt by it."

Margaret remembers the hurt: "I felt like I didn't have a voice. I had been helpful and encouraging of Wayne to finish his different degrees, but when we moved to Minnesota, my dad had just died, so I wanted to put down roots, and it felt like a really safe place. And then leaving there and going to Trinity was hard."

Though the move was difficult, Margaret trusted that God was in control of the situation. She said, "I think the Lord wanted Wayne at Trinity, and if I [had] refused to go, I think I would have been disobeying the Lord, and I needed to go ahead and do that with my husband. . . . I think it built character in me and strength in me, and the Lord was really good to us and our kids there."

They eventually met with a counselor to help them work through the hurts, which led Wayne to grow in his love and respect for Margaret: "I think I've grown in my ability to listen to her, and [I have an] immense respect for her wisdom, insight, [and] knowledge of the Lord and the Lord's will." . . . Now, whenever he has any question about his schedule, "the first thing I want to know is her opinion, and then we both pray about it and seek God's help."

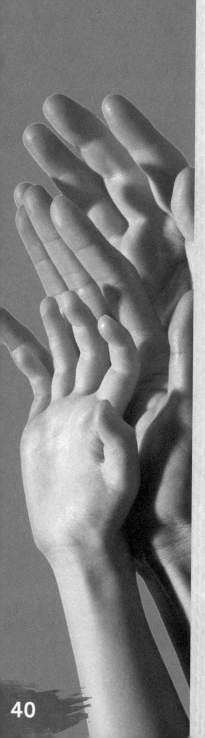

twenty-five ways to spiritually lead your family[8]

1) Pray daily with your wife.

2) Write a love letter that she'd like to receive.

3) Discover her top three needs and over the next twelve months go all out to meet them.

4) Buy her a rose. Take her in your arms. Hold her face gently. Look into her eyes and say, "I'd marry you all over again!"

5) Take her on a weekend getaway.

6) Read the scriptures to her.

7) Replace the "D" word with the "C" word! (D = divorce; C = commitment)

8) Court her.

9) Remain faithful to her.

10) Fulfill your marriage covenant.

11) Have a family time at least one night a week.

12) Use circumstances to teach your children to trust God.

13) Protect your family from evil.

14) Restrain your teenager's passion.

15) Set spiritual goals for your children.

16) Take your children on mission trips.

17) Catch your kids doing something right.

18) Date your daughters.

19) Inspect what you expect.

20) Do a Proverbs breakfast Bible study with your teens (fifteen and older).

21) Hug and kiss your sons and daughters.

22) Ask your children for forgiveness when you fail them.

23) Pray with them.

24) Call them to a spiritual mission to do what God wants to do with their lives.

25) Persevere and don't quit.

what is a woman's role in marriage?

The Family Manifesto for wives:

We believe God has charged each wife to fulfill the responsibility of being her husband's "helper." We believe a wife will give an account to God for how she has loved, respected, and given support to her husband. We uphold the biblical truth that she is of equal value with her husband before God. We reject the notion that a wife should assume the leadership responsibilities of her husband. Likewise, we reject the notion that a wife should passively defer to the dominance of her husband. We believe that her responsibility is to willingly and intelligently affirm, respect, and submit to her husband as the leader in the relationship and in his vocational calling. Therefore, we are committed to exhorting a wife to be in support of her husband by accepting and excelling in her responsibility as his helper (Genesis 2:18–25; Ephesians 5:22–33; Colossians 3:18; 1 Peter 3:1–6; Proverbs 31:10–12).

"The fact that I am a woman does not make me a different kind of Christian, but the fact that I am a Christian does make me a different kind of woman. For I have accepted God's idea of me, and my whole life is an offering back to Him of all that I am, and all that He wants me to be."

—Elisabeth Elliot, *Let Me Be a Woman*

Q&A: a wife's job description[9]

Q: I've heard a lot of differing opinions on a wife's role in marriage. What is a wife's job description? What are the duties and responsibilities involved?

Barbara Rainey: Now, after many years of marriage, I would say that a wife's role in marriage can be summed up in three words: love, support, and respect.

In Titus 2:4, older women are instructed to train the younger women to "love their husbands." Initially that's an easy job, because most of us get married while we're in love. After the feelings fade, though, we have to remember that love is a commitment.

Secondly, we are to support our husbands. Ephesians 5:22 says, "Wives, submit to your husbands as to the Lord." To submit to your husband's leadership is to support his leadership. It means being an encouraging, believing wife who allows her husband to be the leader in the family. It doesn't mean being a doormat. You should share your opinions, your thoughts and feelings, and make decisions together. Ultimately, though, you support your husband's decisions.

Finally, a wife should respect her husband. Ephesians 5:33 commands, "The wife must respect her husband." There are times when that is a hard job; you may not feel that your husband is worthy of respect. However, you are still commanded to respect him. Even if there are many things that he has done wrong, you can find something to respect. Try to remember what you respected about him when you were dating. Does he work hard to financially support the family? Does he play ball with your child?

He may not be doing all that you wish he were doing, but you have to focus positively on the things that he is doing. Verbalize to him your appreciation. When you affirm him and let him know that you value his work, it will be easier for him to continue to lead lovingly.

Proverbs 14:1 says that "the wise woman builds her house, but the foolish tears it down with her own hands" (NASB). As a wife, you have power to create or destroy your relationship with your husband. In your attitude, remember that God is in control, and you can trust him. Also remember that you have to choose to obey God through honoring and obeying your husband. In these ways, you can build a strong house.

defining a wife's role

 BEING A HELPER: A woman is called to be a "helper" in the marriage relationship.

- God is called a "helper" in Scripture (Psalm 121:1–2). If God calls Himself "helper," it shows it is not a derogatory term.

    "From where does my help come? My help comes from the LORD, who made heaven and earth." –Psalm 121:1–2

- Helping involves a willing followership, not in a mindless way, but in a vigorous, robust, feminine way that comes alongside a husband as a partner.

 RESPECT: Wives are called to respect their husbands (Ephesians 5:33).

- There is no more powerful attitude that a wife can have toward her husband than respect.

- Respect is shown not just with words but also with actions, and it flows from an attitude of the heart.

    "The wise woman builds her house, but the foolish tears it down with her own hands." — Proverbs 14:1 (NASB)

Wives: What are five ways I can show my husband I respect him?

1)
2)
3)
4)
5)

 CHEERING HIM ON: Women are called to encourage their husbands to lead their families well.

- For most men, their deepest fear is failure, and their deepest need is the confidence to know they can succeed, the kind of confidence only a wife can provide.

- Even when a husband makes mistakes, he needs encouragement for the ways he is trying to lead.

 SUBMITTING: Submission means following leadership.

- The negative tendency in many marriages is for a man to retreat from leadership, and a wife to step in. And while she may be plenty competent to make good decisions, she is still replacing the role that God outlined in Scripture.

- Biblical submission does not violate the personality that God has given a woman but calls her to live out her personality to its fullest, as God intended.

what is biblical submission?[10]

by Bunny Wilson

- Biblically, *submission* means to yield to people, precepts, and principles that have been placed in our lives by God as an authority.

- Women do not have to submit to anything abusive or immoral. A boss cannot ask her to sign false documents; her husband cannot ask her to sign a false tax return.

- Submission is not an ominous, oppressive force that hangs over a marriage. Rather, it should lead to thoughtful, fruitful discussions about all areas of life.

- Submission is powerful because it operates on pure faith. The act of submitting says, "I believe that God sees all, hears all, knows all, and He will intervene on my behalf."

- A wife cannot say, "I don't have to submit to your final authority if you don't love me as Christ loved the church." She yields to her husband's final decision because that's what God's Word teaches, and she'll learn how power is released when she does that.

- Being submissive can help a husband grow spiritually: "[My husband] said one day in a radio interview . . . , 'When Bunny decided to become submissive, it put the fear of God in my heart because I knew I was no longer contending with her; I was dealing directly with God.'"

- How does one become submissive? You decide to implement the principle in your life. You choose to submit by faith.

- What if I submit and my husband makes a mistake? Your husband is not perfect, and there will be times when he makes a bad decision. You could say to him, "I told you so," or you can say, "Anybody can make a mistake. What can I do to help you fix it?" When we forgive a person's mistakes, it bonds them to us, and it makes the relationship even dearer and nearer.

"Women come up to me all the time and say, 'I don't know how I'm going to do this. I'm a strong woman.' God loves strong women. You know why? Because He knows that once we understand a principle and it's clear, we're just as strong toward submission as we were toward rebellion." —Bunny Wilson

what if your husband doesn't lead?[11]

1) Don't nag. Love him for who he is. Being nagged at is like being nibbled to death by a duck.

2) Don't plot. Instead, pray for him.

3) Don't look for him to obey God perfectly every time—give him grace and forgiveness.

4) Don't tear him down for who he isn't and what he doesn't do. Build him up, even when you think he doesn't deserve it.

5) Don't listen to ungodly counsel that tells you to quit. Surround yourself with Christians who will encourage you to fulfill your marriage vows.

6) Pray that your spouse will be surrounded by godly Christians who will love him and share with him what he needs to hear. (Don't do it yourself. Let God do it.)

COMPLETING the Picture

- I will seek to follow God's design rather than the cultural definition of marriage.

- I choose to honor my spouse as equal in value and yet also to esteem the way God has designed him or her differently from me.

- **Husbands:** I will strive to lead my wife lovingly and sacrificially.

- **Wives:** I will strive to respect and support my husband.

group discussion questions

1) What was the most thought-provoking concept you heard in this session?

2) Describe what is meant by the 50/50 marriage plan. Why is this approach destined to fail?

3) Read Ephesians 5:22–30. Describe the man's role in marriage. Describe the woman's role.

4) The point was made that a man can make his wife's role easier or more difficult by the way he leads. Do you agree? What makes the difference between a man who is easy to follow—as a husband—and one who is not?

5) On the video, Mary Kassian said, "Submission doesn't violate my personality as a woman. As we are more conformed to the image of Jesus Christ, we discover that responsiveness as women feels good and is actually more of who we are."

   Describe some of the influences or circumstances that can make submission difficult for a wife.

   Describe some of the ways that submission benefits a marriage.

6) This session is summed up with the phrase: *equal value, distinct roles.* Describe what this means from a biblical perspective. (The following scriptures may be helpful: Genesis 2:18–25; Proverbs 31:10–12; Ephesians 5:22–33; Colossians 3:18–19; 1 Timothy 5:8; 1 Peter 3:1–7.)

Prepare for your next group meeting by looking over pages 50–60 in your workbook.

Date-Night Ideas

- Head to a place that offers dance lessons. Do some digging to find out what's available.

- Invest in a six-week class at a local studio for the two of you.

- Send the kids to a friend or relative, or wait until they're in bed for the night; then turn on your favorite music and dance in your living room.

Date-Night Discussion

Before the date, do the following on your own:

1. Review the four reasons the 50/50 marriage plan is destined to fail (see page 33). Identify any of these that may be present in your marriage.

2. Read through the definition of your role and your spouse's role in marriage (find husband's role on page 35 and wife's on page 43).

3. Thinking of your own role, use a scale of 1–10 to rate yourself in each area (1=lowest, 10=highest).

4. Again, thinking of your own role, describe ways you would like your spouse to help you become more successful in each area.

5. Husbands, complete the list on page 37 regarding five ways you could sacrifice more for your wife. Wives, complete your list on page 43 regarding five ways you can show your husband respect.

On the Date:

1. Talk about some of the "sources" that shaped your way of viewing roles in marriage (parents, extended family, sitcoms, movies, biblical teaching, etc.), and whether those were good examples or poor ones.

2. Discuss your response to the second portion of question 1 that you answered on your own. (The purpose of this discussion is not to accuse your spouse of ways that you feel he or she is letting you down but to sincerely ask for help.)

3. Share your answers to question 3 that you answered on your own.

4. Pray together that God would give you the grace and patience to work together and to encourage each other in your God-given roles. Thank God for bringing you together.

LOVE
Interrupted

Communication and Conflict

> "If you argue and rankle and contradict, you may achieve a victory sometimes; but it will be an empty victory because you will never get your opponent's good will."
> —Benjamin Franklin

the BIG brush strokes

- Conflict is common to all marriages.

- The goal is not to be conflict-free but to learn to handle conflict correctly when it occurs.

- Healthy conflict resolution occurs when couples are willing to seek and grant forgiveness.

dealing with **anger**

"The anger of man does not produce the righteousness that God requires." —James 1:20

- The source of our anger is within each of us. No one else can "make us angry."

- Conflict occurs when our desires aren't fulfilled—when we don't get what we want.

    - Our rights have been violated.
    - Our expectations haven't been met.
    - We have been hurt.

- Our unfulfilled desires lead to fighting and quarreling.

- Our unfulfilled desires may result in **ANGER**.

"Anger undealt with kills relationships . . . [and] marriages."
—Bryan Loritts

- For conflict to be resolved, both husband and wife must be committed to oneness.

what causes quarrels AND fights among YOU? is it not this, that your PASSIONS ARE AT WAR WITHIN YOU? YOU desire and DO NOT HAVE, so YOU murder. YOU covet and cannot OBTAIN, so you fight and quarrel. YOU do not have, because YOU do not ask.

James 4:1–2

more insight

James 4:1—At the source of our quarrels and anger is our "passions." The Greek word used here is also behind our English word for "hedonism," the belief that "pleasure or happiness is the sole or chief good in life."[1] God has wired us to seek pleasure, but pleasure should not be pursued at the expense of obeying Him (Psalm 37:4; 1 Samuel 15:22). To truly get at the source of our "quarrels," one must ask, "Am I pursuing the pleasure of self-fulfillment or pleasure in Christ?"

James 4:2—Murder, fights, and quarrels: three responses to the inner battle of our passions. Murder is the extreme, yet Jesus reminds us that the outward action of murder begins in the heart (Matthew 5:21–22). Quarrels, though not as serious as murder, are often rooted in the same desires for control and manipulation. Efforts to manipulate could often be avoided by simply asking God and our spouse for wisdom regarding our desires. We need to bring our desires before God, genuinely seeking His direction, and "he will give you the desires of your heart" (Psalm 37:4).

Q&A:
Should children see parents argue?[2]

Q: Is it appropriate to resolve conflict in front of younger children?

Barbara Rainey: **Many parents set a policy of not arguing in front of their kids. There are some good points about this policy, but I also think it is good for our children to see us disagree and have an argument, as long as we keep those to a minimum and don't frighten the kids or make them feel insecure. Kids learn how to resolve conflict by watching us do it.**

If you find that small issues tend to quickly escalate into a heated argument in your marriage, then try one of the following tips the next time you're facing a conflict:

- Take a deep breath to stay relaxed.

- Look the other person in the eye, with both of you sitting or standing.

- Speak softly and slowly. ("A soft answer turns away wrath" [Proverbs 15:1].)

- Keep your legs and arms uncrossed. Do not clench your fists or purse your lips.

- Keep reminding yourself: "We *can* find a win-win resolution to this," and remind the other person of this too.

- Watch your language. Words that escalate a conflict are *never, always, unless, can't, won't, don't, should,* and *shouldn't.* Words that de-escalate a conflict are *maybe, perhaps, sometimes, what if, it seems like, I feel, I think,* and *I wonder.* ("So also the tongue is a small member, yet it boasts of great things. How great a forest is set ablaze by such a small fire!" [James 3:5].)

- Affirm and acknowledge the other person's position.

- Ask questions that encourage the other person to look for a solution. Ask open-ended questions rather than ones that will evoke a yes or no response.

confronting in love

- Because we are fallen creatures, we can expect conflict in marriage.

- There are many things in marriage that are not worth fighting about. ("Love covers a multitude of sins" [1 Peter 4:8].)

- However, there are things that, over time, need to be addressed.

- We have a responsibility to lovingly confront when issues are undermining our relationship.

when preparing to confront

- Examine your heart (Matthew 7:4).

- Spend time in prayer.

- Check your motives.

- Choose your timing wisely.

when it's time to confront

- Speak the truth in love (Ephesians 4:15).

- Choose words carefully (Ephesians 4:29).

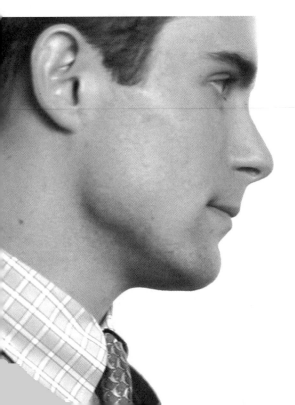

what to consider when preparing to confront

🍂 Is it worth it? Can I just let it go? ("Good sense makes one slow to anger, and it is his glory to overlook an offense" [Proverbs 19:11].)

🍂 What pattern or habit of mine contributed to the problem?

🍂 Have I spent time praying about this issue?

🍂 Is this the right time to confront?

🍂 What's my motivation? Am I trying to

- retaliate—or—restore?
- punish—or—pursue peace?

🍂 Am I "speaking the truth in love" (Ephesians 4:15)?

🍂 Choose words carefully and with humility. ("Let no corrupting talk come out of your mouths, but only such as is good for building up, as fits the occasion, that it may give grace to those who hear" [Ephesians 4:29].)

🍂 Remember, the goal of loving confrontation is to restore ONENESS in your marriage. ("Brothers, if anyone is caught in any transgression, you who are spiritual should restore him in a spirit of gentleness. Keep watch on yourself, lest you too be tempted" [Galatians 6:1].)

confronting winston

Winston Churchill, the prime minister of Britain during World War II, was known for his passion and brilliance. His wife, Clementine, wrote the following letter to lovingly confront him about his uncharacteristically harsh treatment of others around him:[4]

> *My darling . . . I hope you will forgive me if I tell you something that I feel you ought to know. One of the men in your entourage (a devoted friend) has been to me and told me that there is a danger of your being generally disliked by your colleagues and subordinates because of your rough, sarcastic, and overbearing manner. . . . I was astonished and upset, because in all these years I have been accustomed to all those who have worked with and under you, loving you—I said this and was told, "No doubt it's the strain."*
>
> *My darling Winston, I must confess that I have noticed a deterioration in your manner, and you are not so kind as you used to be.*
>
> *It is for you to give the orders, and if they are bungled . . . you can sack anyone and everyone. Therefore, with this terrific power, you must combine urbanity, kindness, and if possible, Olympic calm. You used to quote: "One can only reign over souls with calmness." . . . I cannot bear that those who serve the country and yourself should not love you as well as admire and respect you.*
>
> *Besides, you won't get the best results by irascibility and rudeness. They will breed either dislike or a slave mentality.*
>
> *Please forgive your loving, devoted, and watchful Clemmie,*
>
> *[P.S.] I wrote this at Chequers last Sunday, tore it up, but here it is now.*

> Set your spouse free from the debt of the offense. (Don't continue to punish your spouse. Forgive and move on!)

seeking forgiveness

🍂 All Christians have the privilege of seeking and granting forgiveness because of what God has done for them.

"Be kind to one another, tenderhearted, forgiving one another, as God in Christ forgave you." **(Ephesians 4:32)**

🍂 Some hindrances to seeking forgiveness are

- lacking time to communicate,
- being proud in relationships,
- being too general about the offense, and
- allowing offenses to pile up.

🍂 When seeking forgiveness

- begin by admitting to God and yourself that you were wrong.
- spend time in prayer.
- be specific.
- accept responsibility for the consequences.
- change: consider the attitudes that may have led to the offense and seek to correct them.

steps to seeking forgiveness

🍂 **Be specific:** "I'm sorry for _____."

🍂 **Repent:** "I was wrong and don't want to do that again."

🍂 **Ask for forgiveness:** "Will you forgive me?"

granting
forgiveness

 True forgiveness is not

- conditional,
- forgetting everything that has happened,
- pretending that something did not happen, or
- an automatic cure for the hurt.

It is

- a choice to set your spouse free from the debt of the offense,
- an attitude of letting go of resentment and vengeance,
- the first step toward a process of rebuilding trust, and
- an act of obedience to God.

steps to granting forgiveness

1) **Do it privately:** Go to God in prayer.

   God, I forgive _____ for hurting me.

2) **Do it publically and specifically:** Go to your spouse and be specific.

   I forgive you for _____.

3) **Do it graciously:** Keep the bigger goal in mind.

   Let's settle this and get on with our relationship.

4) **Do it generously:** Acknowledge your own failings to maintain balance.

   I've done things like that myself.

Learning to forgive and trust your spouse sometimes bring to light the need to forgive someone from your past.
—Ron Deal

Rebuilding trust is not automatic; it takes time, patience, and grace from God.

COMPLETING the Picture

🍂 I choose to believe that conflict is common to all marriages.

🍂 I will seek to handle conflict correctly when it occurs in my marriage.

🍂 I will practice seeking and granting forgiveness with my spouse.

group discussion questions

1) What was the most thought-provoking concept you heard in this session?

2) Read James 4:1. As stated on the video, this scripture doesn't locate the cause of our anger in another person or even in our own past but in our inner passions. Why is it important to understand this in order to deal properly with anger?

3) Discuss some of the ways that anger often manifests itself in marriage.

4) First Peter 4:8 tells us to "keep loving one another earnestly, since love covers a multitude of sins."

   - Do you agree that—as stated on the video—some things just need to be overlooked? Explain why you agree or disagree.

   - What advice would you offer to other couples about choosing which issues to address and which ones to overlook?

5) Healthy communication in marriage includes not only our words but also the heart attitudes behind our words. Read Ephesians 4:15–16.

   - Describe the act of "speaking the truth in love."

   - Describe its opposite—either: (a) speaking truth in unloving ways, or (b) speaking with lies and falsehood.

6) Forgiveness—both the seeking and the granting of it—is essential to marriage. What have you personally learned about forgiveness that would be beneficial for the rest of the group to hear? (Caution: Be careful about sharing anything that happened between you and your spouse that he or she has not given permission to be made known publicly.)

7) Explain the difference between winning an argument and resolving a conflict.

Prepare for your next group meeting by looking over pages 64–74 in your workbook.

Date-Night Ideas

🍁 Think back to a time when you had fun "making up" after an argument. Try to find a creative way to re-create that time together (the making up part!).

🍁 Take kickboxing lessons together.

🍁 Have a water balloon or water gun fight. (Go for it. It's fun!) Play fair: equal arsenal and equal access to water.

🍁 Have a candlelight picnic on your living room floor. Sit close and take turns whispering reasons you love your spouse.

Date-Night Discussion

Before the date, do the following on your own:

1. Read the tips to cooling off that are listed on page 54. Identify those that you feel you typically employ in times of conflict and those that you need to get better at observing.

2. Read the list of things to consider when preparing to confront on page 56. If there are any outstanding conflicts between you and your spouse right now, prayerfully work through this list and determine when and how to deal with it.

3. Spend some time contemplating the great forgiveness that God has given you. Thank Him!

On the Date:

1. Take turns completing this statement: The way my parents resolved conflict was by . . .

2. Identify any unresolved conflicts that you have in your marriage. Purpose to handle them biblically.

3. Take time to share your thoughts from the three questions you answered on your own.

4. Express your gratitude to each other for being willing to work through conflict and for not running away from it.

5. Pray together that God would give you the grace to be humble, patient, and eager to forgive as you have each been forgiven. Thank God for His great and eternal forgiveness.

LOVE

Sizzles

Experiencing Real Intimacy

> "Sex is good because the God who created sex is good. And God is glorified greatly when we receive his gift with thanksgiving and enjoy it the way he meant for it to be enjoyed."
> —Ben Patterson, in *Sex and the Supremacy of Christ*

the BIG brush strokes

- 🖌 God created sex and has a wonderful design in mind.

- 🖌 A satisfying sex life is the result of a satisfying marriage relationship.

- 🖌 The ultimate purpose of sex is to bring glory to God by celebrating our oneness.

God's design for **sex**

> Let your fountain
> **be blessed,**
>   and rejoice in the
>   **wife of your youth,**
>   a lovely deer,
>   **a graceful doe.**
> Let her breasts fill you
> **at all times with**
> delight;
>   **be intoxicated**
>   always in her love.
>
> **—Proverbs 5:18–19**

- The Bible gives *three reasons* for sexual intercourse:

    ✓ **1)** Oneness before God
    2) Pleasure
    3) Procreation

- The ultimate purpose of sex is a celebration of our oneness in the sight of God.

- God created sex and called the union between man and woman "very good" (Genesis 1:31).

- God created sex to be enjoyable, pleasurable, and passionate in marriage.

In the Old Testament, the book of the Song of Solomon captures the romantic relationship between a young man and a young woman. Each of these young lovers writes a letter describing the attributes he or she finds most attractive in the other:

his love letter to her

¹How beautiful are your feet in sandals, O noble daughter! Your rounded thighs are like jewels, the work of a master hand. ²Your navel is a rounded bowl that never lacks mixed wine. Your belly is a heap of wheat, encircled with lilies. ³Your two breasts are like two fawns, twins of a gazelle. ⁴Your neck is like an ivory tower. Your eyes are pools in Heshbon, by the gate of Bath-rabbim. Your nose is like a tower of Lebanon, which looks toward Damascus. ⁵Your head crowns you like Carmel, and your flowing locks are like purple; a king is held captive in the tresses. ⁶How beautiful and pleasant you are, O loved one, with all your delights! ⁷Your stature is like a palm tree, and your breasts are like its clusters. ⁸I say I will climb the palm tree and lay hold of its fruit. Oh may your breasts be like clusters of the vine, and the scent of your breath like apples, ⁹and your mouth like the best wine." —Song of Solomon 7:1–9

nose like a tower of lebanon?

Nothing is more romantic than having your pronounced snout praised or your big belly blessed, right? Well, maybe not. Not having been born in ancient Israel, modern readers find that the meaning of some of these love-letter lines are lost on them. Here is a brief explanation of a few of the trickier sayings:

WHAT IT SAYS	WHAT IT MEANS TODAY
"Eyes are like doves beside streams of water" (5:12)	His eyes are healthy and white, and apparently, the man doesn't mind shedding a tear.
"Cheeks are like beds of spices" (5:13)	His beard smells good enough to kiss!
"Navel is a rounded bowl" (7:2)	She is a dream come true, like a cup of wine that never empties.
"Belly is a heap of wheat" (7:2)	Her skin is a lovely golden brown; it is as beautiful as the flowers of the field.
"Nose is like a tower of Lebanon" (7:4)	Her face is as beautiful as the most majestic mountain in Israel.

10My beloved is radiant and ruddy, distinguished among ten thousand. 11His head is the finest gold; his locks are wavy, black as a raven. 12His eyes are like doves beside streams of water, bathed in milk, sitting beside a full pool. 13His cheeks are like beds of spices, mounds of sweet-smelling herbs. His lips are lilies, dripping liquid myrrh. 14His arms are rods of gold, set with jewels. His body is polished ivory, bedecked with sapphires. 15His legs are alabaster columns, set on bases of gold. His appearance is like Lebanon, choice as the cedars. 16His mouth is most sweet, and he is altogether desirable. This is my beloved and this is my friend, O daughters of Jerusalem." —Song of Solomon 5:10–16

allegorical or literal?

A number of famous people in the history of the church have thought that the Song of Solomon was written as an allegory about Christ's love for the church. Pastor C. J. Mahaney offers a few reasons why we should think otherwise:[1]

1) It is obviously about sex: "Just consider all the sensual and erotic language in the book!"

2) "The Bible never suggests that this book isn't primarily about sex."

3) God's relationship with man is never portrayed as sexual in the Bible.

4) "Spiritualizing the book doesn't work." Some of the statements become very strange if you try to view them symbolically.

5) We should expect to find God giving us guidance in Scripture about such an important topic as sex!

song of solomon and sex

- God intended for us to explore our sexuality within marriage—it's a gift.

- We're not to put sexuality in a box; there's a liberty for creativity, initiative, and pursuit.

- The Song of Solomon is in the Bible to inspire married couples as to what could be.

- A goal of sexual intimacy is to see that your spouse has a wonderful, safe, lovely, profound, and fulfilling experience, and to enjoy your relationship with each other around that experience.

- Sex is not to be given only as a favor or seen as an entitlement.

- We must learn to communicate our expectations for sex with our spouse.

- Sometimes we have to save energy to reserve it for sexual fulfillment.

"Sin corrupts everything . . . [and] it drives couples apart in their physical relationship."

—Dave Harvey

"Sexual intimacy doesn't happen automatically. . . . It means getting to know one's husband or wife, which often takes a long time."

—Russell Moore

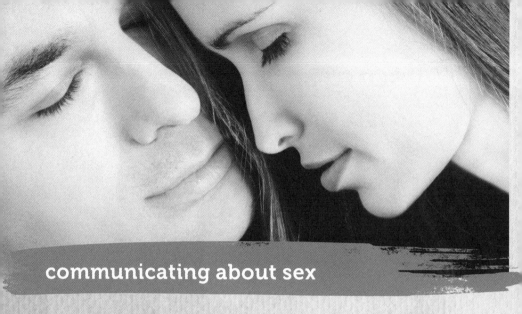

communicating about sex

For some, talking about sex can be awkward or uncomfortable, especially if there have been some bumps in the road in the relationship. But husbands and wives should find freedom and joy in learning to talk openly about likes and dislikes between the sheets. Here are a few ideas for communicating about sex:

- **Pray.** If you are anxious about discussing sex, then spend some time praying for wisdom and for God to soften the heart of your spouse. Pray that God would also help your heart to be in the right place before you approach your spouse.

- **Wait for the right moment.** As in humor, timing is everything in communication. When talking about sensitive subjects, finding the right location and time will help defuse some of the obstacles to good communication.

- **Be clear about your likes and dislikes.** Your spouse cannot read your mind, so if there is something he or she does sexually that you like, make sure to let your spouse know! And though it's more difficult to mention, your spouse needs to know about the turn-offs as well. Your spouse wants to please you in the bedroom, so help him or her know how to do a great job.

- **Use good communication principles.** Avoid using words like "You always . . ." or "You never . . . ," or being accusatory in your tone. Instead, assume the best about your spouse's intentions and desires and use phrases like "I feel like . . ." and "Help me understand. . . ."

- **Learn to flirt!** It is okay to lighten the mood a bit by flirting with each other outside of the bedroom. Discreetly mentioning your desires can help build excitement and anticipation for the big moment.

true intimacy

> "I'm convinced that for most couples, you fix sexual dysfunction outside of the marriage bed." —Paul David Tripp

- Sexual problems are generally a symptom of another problem.

- Sex is like a thermometer in marriage, not a thermostat, in that it measures the health of your intimacy rather than sets it.

- True intimacy happens when you open up areas of your life to your spouse that are not readily available to others.

Sex is like a thermometer . . . it is primarily a by-product of your relational intimacy.

If there is selfishness, irritation, and frustration in your marriage, these things will come into your marriage bed as well.

why sex is so important to your wife[2]

Physical intimacy and romance cultivate emotional intimacy with your wife and give her a sense of security and stability in your relationship and for her as a woman.

When a man shows sexual interest in his wife, she feels pursued and desired. But when romance, tenderness, and sex are not shared, a sense of loneliness sets in that can ultimately result in emotional and sexual temptation.

For most men who lack sexual desire, the primary problem is not inadequate interest or erectile dysfunction; it is a sense of rejection by their wife, physical problems brought on by stress, medication, or depression, or a sense of fear (performance anxiety or the fear of not being wanted sexually). Leaving these issues unresolved will lead to further isolation in a marriage.

A lack of sexual desire for your wife could also be a symptom of a rejection at an earlier point in your marriage. The lingering hurt and thought of being rejected again may seem too great to overcome. You may be withdrawing from her sexually as a strategy to protect yourself. If so, take a step out of the shadows of isolation and into healing with the One who gives "every good and perfect gift" (James 1:17).

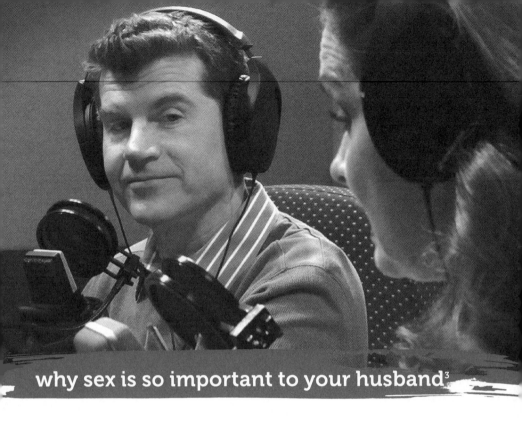

why sex is so important to your husband[3]

🌿 Sexual intimacy with your husband gives both of you the comfort of being known and accepted on a deep level that is unlike any other human relationship.

🌿 A man's sexuality, the very essence of his manhood, is primarily expressed through sexual intercourse.

🌿 Temptation can get a foothold when your husband's sexual needs (including the need to feel desired by his wife) remain unmet (1 Corinthians 7:5).

🌿 Safety and security result in being "naked and not ashamed" as did Adam and Eve (Genesis 2:25).

COMPLETING the *Picture*

- I will seek to follow God's design for sex.

- I commit to working through the issues that may be inhibiting a fully satisfying sexual relationship in our marriage.

- To pursue a satisfying sex life, I will also make the overall health of our marriage a higher priority.

group **discussion** questions

1) What was the most thought-provoking concept you heard in this session?

2) Identify some of the cultural attitudes about sex that could undermine a fulfilling sex life in your marriage.

3) On the video the point was made that couples need to make passion and pleasure priorities in their marriage. Discuss some of the adjustments you've had to make in order to give your sexual relationship its proper place.

4) Read 1 Corinthians 7:3–5. In the context of sexual intimacy in marriage, explain what is meant by: "the wife does not have authority over her own body, but the husband does" and "the husband does not have authority over his own body, but the wife does."

5) Does a good relationship make for good sex, or does good sex make for a good relationship? Explain your answer.

6) When the need comes for you and your spouse to talk about your sexual relationship, what makes it easier for you to talk about it? What makes it more difficult?

Prepare for your next group meeting by looking over pages 78–86 in your workbook.

Date-Night Ideas

🍂 Go to the most romantic restaurant in town.

🍂 Pack a romantic picnic of finger foods you can feed each other.

🍂 Ask your husband to describe the perfect afternoon or evening that would get him "in the mood," and then do your best to create it "to order."

🍂 Ask your wife to describe the perfect afternoon or evening that would get her "in the mood," and then do your best to create it "to order."

Date-Night Discussion

Before the date, do the following on your own:

1. Review Communicating About Sex on page 70.

2. List some of the things that you have had to learn, unlearn, or relearn in order to have a healthy and mutually fulfilling sex life with your spouse.

3. Recall one or two of your "top ten of all time" sexual experiences with your spouse. Be prepared to describe it to him or her on your date.

On the Date:

1. Each of you answer: In my opinion, in order to make our sex life even better, we need to work on . . .

2. Review Communicating About Sex (page 70) together, then have an open discussion about the hopes and desires you have for your sex life. Discuss things like what you like and what you don't, the frequency of your lovemaking, what you can each do to get the other in the mood, etc.

3. Discuss your responses to question 3 that you answered on your own.

4. Pray together. Thank God for the gift of sex in your marriage. Ask Him to make you a good lover—one who seeks to give more than take.

LOVE
Always

Leaving a Lasting Legacy

"Marriage is more than your love for each other. It has a higher dignity and power, for it is God's holy institution through which God wishes to preserve humanity until the end of time. In your love you see only each other in the world; in marriage you are a link in the chain of generations that God, for the sake of his glory, allows to rise and fade away, and calls into his kingdom."

—Dietrich Bonhoeffer, *Letters and Papers from Prison*

the BIG brush strokes

- To leave a godly legacy, we must think about the impact of our lives on future generations.

- Our hope for leaving a lasting legacy is through the gospel of Jesus Christ.

- Leaving a godly legacy requires putting a stake in the ground.

Ten Ideas: Helping Your Marriage Last a Lifetime[1]

The following ten ideas, shared by couples married for fifty years or more, will help your marriage last a lifetime.

1) **You need a Savior.** "We didn't realize that it was two sinners who married each other. Two very sinful people who needed a Savior." (Mona Sproull)

2) **Stay committed to one another.** "Love is not a feeling, it's a commitment . . . no matter what, I will stand by [my wife]." (Charles Powell)

3) **Pray with your spouse.** "Rather than each of us having ourselves at the center of our thinking, there enters a willingness to let God be at the center." (Jerry Bell)

4) **Forgive one another.** "All I could think of was if God could forgive me of all of my sins, who am I not to forgive my husband." (Joan Fortin)

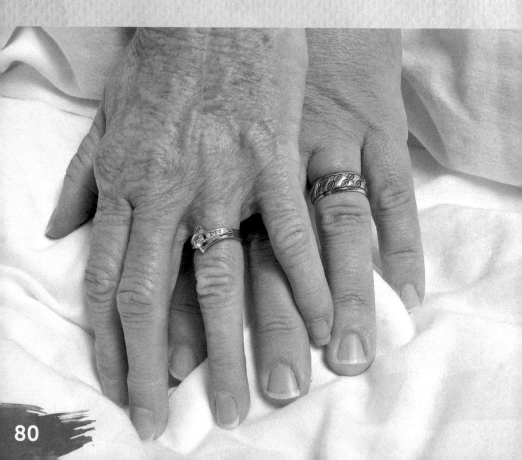

5) **Realize that there's no such thing as a perfect husband or perfect wife.** "Christ has given me understanding and lets me know that everyone does something wrong sometimes." (Mattie Foy)

6) **Have faith that God knows what [He] is doing.** "A lot of people would ask me, 'No children yet?' And I'd say, 'No, but I am sure having a good time telling you how to raise yours.'" (Jodie May)

7) **Trust that God gives grace and direction as you trust [Him].** "How can [parents] trust the Lord when they lose a child? It takes a lot of faith." (Richard Long)

8) **You'll need to make compromises.** "You can't always have your way. I just thought that marriage would be a give-and-take situation." (Nelda Davenport)

9) **Be objective and take the emotion out of problem solving.** "If I say something to you that's disrespectful to you and I don't really know it, you need to trust my heart." (Mona Sproull)

10) **Love your spouse.** "The love comes from God." (Mattie Foy)

leaving a
legacy

Every couple has to make a choice to "put a stake in the ground" and start a new legacy with their family. One of the greatest gifts you can give to the next generation is faithfulness and fidelity in marriage. Consider the following:

- Hope for leaving a lasting legacy is through the gospel of Jesus Christ.

- Your marriage is a picture of the gospel to a watching world.

- Marital relationships are the central glue holding civilization together.

"You are an ancestor to someone yet to come. If you live your life knowing you are an ancestor, that will change the way you make your decisions, the way you live your life, the way you love your wife."

—Albert Mohler

"Children are the living messages we send to a time we will not see."

—Neil Postman,
The Disappearance of Childhood

five essentials in leaving a legacy that will outlive you[2]

by Dennis Rainey

1) **Fear the Lord and obey Him.** Your legacy begins in your heart, in your relationship with God. Psalm 112:1–2 reads: "How blessed is the man who fears the LORD, / Who greatly delights in His commandments. / His descendants will be mighty on earth; / The generation of the upright will be blessed" (NASB).

   On our first Christmas together . . . , Barbara and I [Dennis] gave a gift to God first. These sheets of paper became title deeds to our lives—to our marriage, to our hopes of having children, to our family, to our relationships, to our rights to our lives, to whatever ministry God gave us—we gave everything to Him.

2) **Recognize the world's needs and respond with compassion and action.** In Matthew 9:36 we read: "When he [Jesus] saw the crowds, he had compassion for them." You and your [spouse] need to leave a legacy by being committed to doing something about our world. Many Christians today are walking in the middle of the road; they're so focused on what other people think that they are unwilling to take any risks in order to make an impact for Christ. In light of this, Jamie Buckingham wrote, "The problem with Christians today is that no one wants to kill them anymore."

   When you fly over rows of houses, do you wonder how many people in those homes know Jesus? This year thirty million people will die without hearing the name of Christ. Hundreds of millions will pray to idols. Someone needs to reach these people with the Good News.

John F. Kennedy, in *Profiles in Courage*, described the need for courageous people: "Some men show courage throughout the whole of their lives. Others sail with the wind until the decisive moment when their conscience and events propel them into the center of the storm." If you want to leave a lasting legacy, you need to act with courage to reach out to those in need.

3) **Pray as a couple that God will use you to accomplish His purposes.** As recorded in 1 Chronicles 4:10, Jabez prayed, "Oh that thou wouldest bless me indeed, and enlarge my coast, and that thine hand might be with me, and that thou wouldest keep *me* from evil" (KJV).

What did Jabez ask God to do? Bless him. Give him new turf and enlarge his sphere of influence. Keep him from temptation. Stay with him. Pray this prayer with your [spouse], and at the end of the year, see how different your lives will be.

4) **Help your [spouse] be a better steward of his gifts and abilities.** Help [your spouse] recognize how God has used his gifts and abilities in the past. Serving others? Teaching the Scripture? Advising a Christian ministry?

Help him plug into the local church, which needs committed laymen and women who have strong, godly character and a vision for their communities.

Help him recognize his convictions. Thomas Carlyle says, "Conviction is worthless until it can convert itself into daily conduct." Help your [spouse] determine what he is willing to die for so he can ultimately determine what he can live for.

5) **Ask God to give your children a sense of purpose, direction, and mission.** The challenge here is to leave your children a heritage, not just an inheritance. As someone once said, "Our children are the living messages we send to a time we will not see."

Dignity Through Destiny

David Livingstone, the missionary to Africa, said, "I will go anywhere, as long as it is forward." And by moving forward and advancing God's kingdom, he undoubtedly also advanced his sense of dignity.

Gaining a vision and a direction in life will yield significance to your [spouse's] life as well, especially if the omnipotent God of the universe has set that heading and direction. In fact, true vision, direction, and destiny can come only from the One who controls not only the present but also the future. By discovering your eternal destiny, you will begin to build lasting dignity in your lives. The internal awareness of that God-ordained dignity will enhance the self-esteem of every member of your family.

The challenge is the same for all of us. Will we follow Christ and fulfill [His] call and vision for our lives? Just as we found spiritual life in no other Person than Jesus Christ, so we find a dignity like no other in the destiny [He] provides.

Every MAN leaves a lasting INFLUENCE THAT WILL affect future generations for centuries to come.

NOT ALL LEGACIES ARE THE same. what kind of a legacy WILL YOU LEAVE BEHIND?

a spiritual LEGACY is one that MONEY can't buy AND TAXES can't take away.

A spiritual LEGACY is passing down to the next GENERATION WHAT MATTERS MOST.

Steven J. Lawson—*The Legacy*

COMPLETING the *Picture*

- I must think about the impact of my life on future generations.

- My hope for leaving a lasting legacy is through the gospel of Jesus Christ.

- I will begin to leave a godly legacy by "putting a stake in the ground" today.

group discussion questions

1) What was the most thought-provoking concept you heard in this session?

2) Who is affected by your marriage? (Identify them by name or by groups/categories.)

3) Describe the legacy that you hope to leave for your children, grandchildren, and the generations beyond.

4) Read Psalm 112:1–2. Describe some of the actions that you need to take or the adjustments you want to make in order to start building a godly legacy today.

5) Perhaps you have not received a strong legacy, but this does not mean that you cannot leave one. Perhaps God is calling you and your spouse to "turn the tide" for the sake of your descendants. If you have the freedom to share, how can the other group members pray for you?

6) Think of those in your life whose marriage you admire, especially a couple that has been married for thirty years or more. Describe something about their marriage that you want to be true of yours.

the art of **marriage** team

Jose and Michelle Alvarez
Jose played professional baseball for sixteen years and began competing professionally in golf in 2006. He is part of the Fellowship of Christian Athletes Golf Ministry, serving in several capacities, including chaplain for the Nationwide Tour and assisting in national outreach events. Michelle works with an event planning and management team and is an administrative assistant.

Voddie Baucham
Dr. Voddie Baucham Jr. wears many hats. He is a husband, father, pastor, author, professor, conference speaker, and church planter. He currently serves as pastor of preaching at Grace Family Baptist Church in Spring, Texas. He and his wife, Bridget, have six children.

Julie Boyd
Bruce and Julie serve in the concert and arts outreach of Campus Crusade for Christ's Keynote ministry. The Boyds, with their children, minister through music at events that focus on family and marriage issues. Bruce received his Bachelor of Arts degree in music education from the University of Illinois. Julie received a Bachelor's degree in Business Management from Texas Wesleyan University, and now home schools their three boys. The Boyds live in Fishers, Indiana.

Bryan Carter
Bryan L. Carter (M.A., Dallas Theological Seminary) is the senior pastor of Concord Church in Dallas, Texas. He is active in the city of Dallas in numerous capacities and hosts a national conference on expository preaching. He is married to his college sweetheart, Stephanie; they have three children.

Raymond and Donna Causey
Raymond, former director of Urban Family Ministries, now pastors a church in Atlanta. He received his Bachelor of Arts in communications and biblical studies from Biola University, and authored *Changing for Good*. His wife, Donna, is a homemaker, Bible teacher, and mentor.

Michael Easley
Dr. Michael Easley is an author, speaker, former president of the Moody Bible Institute, pastor, and conference speaker. Michael and his wife, Cindy, have four children and live near Nashville, Tennessee, where Michael serves as the lead pastor of Fellowship Bible Church.

Brian and Jen Goins

Brian and Jennifer Goins work with couples in Charlotte, North Carolina, where Brian is a pastor at Renaissance Bible Church. He also writes for various nonprofit organizations. Jennifer is a homemaker who enjoys leading Bible study groups, cooking, and keeping track of her family's memories and milestones. The Goinses have three children.

Wayne and Margaret Grudem

Dr. Wayne Grudem is a research professor of theology and biblical studies at Phoenix Seminary. He was a member of the translation oversight committee for the English Standard Version of the Bible, and general editor for the ESV Study Bible. Margaret is a full-time homemaker and leads discipleship groups for wives of pastors. The Grudems have three grown sons and two grandchildren.

Dave Harvey

Dr. Dave Harvey (D. Min., Westminster Theological Seminary) is responsible for church planting, church care, and international expansion for Sovereign Grace Ministries, having served on the leadership team since 1995. He is the author of *When Sinners Say "I Do"* and is a contributing author to *Worldliness: Resisting the Seduction of a Fallen World*. Dave lives in West Chester, Pennsylvania, with his wife, Kimm. They have four children.

Mary Kassian

Mary Kassian is an award-winning author, internationally renowned speaker, and a distinguished professor at The Southern Baptist Theological Seminary. She has published several books and Bible studies, including *The Feminist Mistake*. A graduate of Rehabilitation Medicine from the University of Alberta, Canada, Mary has also studied systematic theology at the doctoral level and taught courses at seminaries throughout North America.

Bryan Loritts

Bryan is the lead pastor of Fellowship Memphis Church, a multicultural church ministering to the urban Memphis community. Bryan has a master's degree in theology and is currently working on his PhD. In addition to serving the community of Memphis, Bryan's ministry takes him across the country as a speaker. He wrote *God on Paper* and was a contributing author to *Great Preaching*. Bryan and his wife, Korie, have three sons.

Crawford Loritts

Dr. Crawford Loritts is the senior pastor of Fellowship Bible Church in Roswell, Georgia, the daily host of the radio program *Living a Legacy*, internationally known Bible teacher, and author. His books include *A Passionate Commitment, Leadership as an Identity* and *Never Walk Away*. Crawford and his bride, Karen, have been married forty years. They have four grown children and five grandchildren.

Robyn McKelvy

Robyn and her husband, Ray, live in Brentwood, Tennessee, where Ray serves as a community group pastor at Fellowship Bible Church. Robyn, a mother of eight children, keeps busy with cooking, cleaning, laundry, counseling, mentoring, and writing. She has finished her first book and awaits its publication.

Tony and Venita Mitchell

Tony is chief financial officer of Morrison Management Specialists. He is a Certified Public Accountant (CPA), a board member of a national foodservice nonprofit organization, and a public speaker. Venita, also a CPA, has worked in public and private accounting, is director of women's ministry at her local church, and has been a full-time homemaker since 1988.

Al Mohler

Dr. R. Albert Mohler Jr. serves as president of the Southern Baptist Theological Seminary. A leader among American evangelicals, Dr. Mohler is widely sought as a columnist and cultural commentator. He is the author of numerous books, including *Words from the Fire*, and is the host of two programs, *Thinking in Public* and *The Briefing*. He also writes a popular blog. He is married to Mary; they have two children.

Hans and Star Molegraaf

Hans and Star have a powerful testimony of God's ability to revive a dead marriage. They served with FamilyLife for four years and now provide marriage help to hurting couples through their own marriage ministry, Marriage Revolution. They and their six children live near Houston, Texas.

Russell Moore

Dr. Russell D. Moore is the senior vice president for Academic Administration and dean of the school of theology at The Southern Baptist Theological Seminary in Louisville, Kentucky. He is also a preaching pastor at Highview Baptist Church in Louisville, a writer *(Adopted for Life)* and speaker. He is a senior editor of *Touchstone: A Journal of Mere Christianity* and also blogs regularly at *russellmoore.com*. He and his wife, Maria, have four sons.

Bill and Pam Mutz

Bill is the president of Lakeland Automall in Lakeland, Florida. He has been involved with the ministries of FamilyLife and Promise Keepers. Bill and Pam serve in their local church and various community boards. Pam graduated as a physical education major and is a commissioned Centurion through Prison Fellowship. She currently mentors and teaches women's Bible studies. Bill and Pam are the parents of twelve children.

Dennis and Barbara Rainey

Dr. Dennis Rainey serves as president of FamilyLife and hosts the nationally syndicated *FamilyLife Today®* radio program. Barbara is an artist and writer, and enjoys creating resources for women and families. The Raineys have written over twenty-five books together, including bestsellers *Moments Together for Couples* and *Building Your Mate's Self-Esteem.* They have six children and numerous grandchildren.

Jeff and Debbie Schreve

Jeff is the senior pastor of First Baptist Church in Texarkana, Texas, and the founder of the radio and TV ministry, From His Heart Ministries. Debbie is a housewife and works as the executive secretary for From His Heart Ministries.

Jeff Schulte

Jeff is a Fellow and Executive Director of the Sage Hill Institute, an initiative for authentic Christian leadership. He speaks nationally and internationally on a variety of men's issues including biblical masculinity, fatherhood, spiritual formation, leadership, and relational authenticity. Jeff and his wife, Brenda, are the parents of six children and reside in Anchorage, Alaska.

Bobby Scott

Bobby Scott is the teaching pastor of Los Angeles Community Bible Church, instructor at the Los Angeles Bible Training School, and a visiting lecturer at The Master's Seminary. He holds a MDiv. and ThM. from The Master's Seminary. Scott is the general editor of *Secret Sex Wars*, a biblical anthology from seven Christian leaders. He cherishes his family—his devoted wife, Naomi, and their six children.

Paul David Tripp

Dr. Paul Tripp has been a church planter, traveling musician, painter, teacher, author, and founder of a Christian school. He currently serves as the president of Paul Tripp Ministries, and is on the pastoral staff at Tenth Presbyterian Church in Philadelphia. He is also professor of pastoral life and care at the Redeemer Seminary in Dallas. Paul and Luella, his wife of almost forty years, have four children.

Christopher and Susan Willard

Chris and Susan Willard met at the University of Massachusetts where Chris studied history and Susan studied painting and design. Chris has an MBA and works as a consultant and coach with Leadership Network, which is dedicated to accelerating the impact of high capacity leaders. Susan is an interior decorator and owns her own business, Fabulous Interiors. They have three children and live in Orlando.

Dave and Ann Wilson

Dave received a Master of Divinity degree from the International School of Theology and serves as teaching pastor to the Kensington Community Church in Troy, Michigan. Inducted into the Men's Athletic Hall of Fame at Ball State University, Dave is also chaplain to the Detroit Lions. Ann ministers to wives of professional athletes and is a homemaker.

notes

SESSION 1

1. Bill Adler, ed., "When I Get Married," *McCall's*, June 1979, 107, quoted in Dennis Rainey and Barbara Rainey, *Staying Close* (Nashville: Thomas Nelson, 2003), 109.

2. Relationships Australia and Credit Union Australia, *Relationships Indicators Survey 2008: Issues and Concerns That Australians Have in Their Relationships Today* (Deakin, ACT, Australia: Relationships Australia, 2008), 13, relationships.com.au/resources/pdfs/reports-submissions/ra-rel-ind-survey-2008-report.pdf.

3. Paula Y. Goodwin, William D. Mosher, and Anjani Chandra, "Marriage and Cohabitation in the United States: A Statistical Portrait Based on Cycle 6 (2002) of the National Survey of Family Growth," National Center for Health Statistics, *Vital Health Statistics* 23, no. 28 (2010): 2, www.cdc.gov/nchs/data/series/sr_23/sr23_028.pdf.

4. Ibid., 19, 35, 36.

SESSION 2

1. John Gottman, *Why Marriages Succeed or Fail: And How You Can Make Yours Last* (New York: Simon and Schuster, 1995), 29.

SESSION 3

1. Tim Satchell, *Astaire: The Biography* (London: Arrow, 1988), 127.

2. John Mueller, "She Changed Partners and Danced," *New York Times,* October 20, 1991, nytimes.com/ 1991/10/20/books/she-changed-partners-and-danced.html.

3. Adapted from Dennis Rainey and Barbara Rainey, *Starting Your Marriage Right* (Nashville: Thomas Nelson, 2000), 7–9. Used by permission.

4. Yahoo! HotJobs annual job-satisfaction survey, cited in "Top 10 Qualities of a Good Boss," RISMedia, January 10, 2008, www.rismedia.com/2008-01-09/top-10-qualities-of-a-good-boss/.

5. Adapted from Dennis Rainey and Barbara Rainey, *Building Your Mate's Self-Esteem* (Nashville: Thomas Nelson, 1995), 250. Used by permission.

6. Wayne Grudem, *Evangelical Feminism and Biblical Truth* (Sisters, OR: Multnomah, 2004), 544.

7. Wayne and Margaret Grudem, interview by Bob Lepine, March 10, 2010.

8. Adapted from Dennis Rainey, "25 Ways to Spiritually Lead Your Family," FamilyLife, accessed November 11, 2010, www.familylife .com/site/apps/nlnet/content3.aspx?c=dnJ HKLNnFoG&b=3871753&ct=4640205.

9. Adapted from Dennis Rainey and Barbara Rainey, "A Wife's Job Description," FamilyLife, accessed October 21, 2010,www.familylife .com/site/apps/nlnet/content3.aspx?c= dnJHKLNnFoG&b=3781105&ct=4639815.

10. Summarized and quoted from a speech by Bunny Wilson, "Liberating Submission," Building Strong Families in Your Church Pastors Conference (Dallas: March 2000).

11. Adapted from Rainey, *Building Your Mate's Self-Esteem*, 181.

SESSION 4

1. *Merriam-Webster's Collegiate Dictionary*, 11th ed., s.v. "hedonism."

2. Dennis Rainey and Barbara Rainey, "Q&A: Should Children See Parents Argue?" FamilyLife, accessed November 11, 2010, www.familylife.com/site/apps/nlnet/content3.aspx?c =dnJHKLNnFoG&b=3855925&ct=4639787.

3. List taken from William DeJong, U.S Department of Justice, *Building the Peace: The Resolving Conflict Creatively Program* (Washington, DC: Government Printing Office, 1993), NCJ-149549, 6.

4. Adapted from Jon Meacham, *Franklin and Winston: An Intimate Portrait of an Epic Friendship* (New York: Random House, 2003), 64–65.

SESSION 5

1. Adapted from C. J. Mahaney, *Sex, Romance, and the Glory of God* (Wheaton, IL: Crossway, 2004), 11–13.

2. Adapted from Dennis Rainey and Barbara Rainey, *Rekindling the Romance* (Nashville: Thomas Nelson, 2004), 255–61. Used by permission.

3. Ibid., 57–67.

SESSION 6

1. Mary May Larmoyeux, "10 Ideas: Helping Your Marriage Last a Lifetime," FamilyLife, accessed October 28, 2010, www.familylife .com/site/apps/nlnet/content3.aspx?c=dnJ HKLNnFoG&b=3781065&ct=5722439.

2. Adapted from Dennis Rainey and Barbara Rainey, *Building Your Mate's Self-Esteem* (Nashville: Thomas Nelson, 1995), 230–232. Reprinted by permission.

We enjoyed The Art of Marriage® small-group series. What can we do next?

FamilyLife® is here to help with practical, biblical resources for your marriage and family. Learn about these and many other resources at **FamilyLife.com**.

- **Gloo App:** Continue your Art of Marriage experience on your mobile device or tablet. Visit TheArtofMarriage.com/mobile.

- **The Art of Marriage® video event:** A weekend video event that expands on the concepts presented in The Art of Marriage small-group series.

- **The Art of Marriage® Connect:** Start or join a small group with one of our topical group studies for couples.

- **The Smart Stepfamily:** Helps couples facilitate the "blending process," gives tips for raising stepkids, and offers solutions for everyday living.

- **Marriage Oneness:** Video-based, eight-session study equips couples to grow in true intimacy, connection, and purpose.

- **Weekend to Remember® marriage getaway:** A two-and-a-half day getaway for couples to learn marriage-enhancing principles with a healthy dose of fun.

- **FamilyLife Today® radio broadcast:** Find daily encouragement on your local Christian stations.

FamilyLife would like to know more about your experience with The Art of Marriage small-group series. Please complete our survey at **www.surveymonkey.com/s/TAOMSmallGroup**.

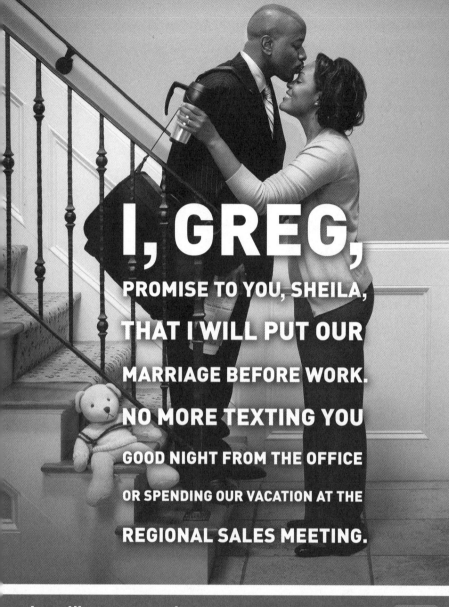

I, GREG,

PROMISE TO YOU, SHEILA,

THAT I WILL PUT OUR

MARRIAGE BEFORE WORK.

NO MORE TEXTING YOU

GOOD NIGHT FROM THE OFFICE

OR SPENDING OUR VACATION AT THE

REGIONAL SALES MEETING.

ABOUT FAMILYLIFE®

FamilyLife® is a donor-supported nonprofit ministry headquartered in Little Rock, Arkansas, whose mission is to develop godly marriages and families who change the world one home at a time. Cofounded in 1976 by Dennis and Barbara Rainey, FamilyLife has strengthened millions of marriages and families through numerous resources, including:

- ▶ Weekend to Remember® marriage getaways
- ▶ *FamilyLife Today*® and *Real FamilyLife*® *with Dennis Rainey* radio broadcasts
- ▶ The Art of Marriage® Connect group studies for couples
- ▶ The Art of Marriage® video event and video series
- ▶ Stepping Up® video event and video series (for men)
- ▶ Passport2Purity®
- ▶ FamilyLife.com
- ▶ FamilyLife Blended™
- ▶ Hope for Orphans®

FamilyLife works in more than one hundred countries around the world and utilizes a volunteer network of more than twenty thousand people. They help bring God's message to others through the practical application of time-tested techniques and teachings that are based on biblical principles.

Find us online for more information.

 FamilyLife.com

 facebook.com/familylifeministry

 @FamilyLifeOrg